This is Me! Mel B!

Errol Lloyd

Illustrated by Derek Brazell

OXFORD
UNIVERSITY PRESS

OXFORD

UNIVERSITY PRESS

Great Clarendon Street, Oxford OX2 6DP

Oxford University Press is a department of the University of Oxford.
It furthers the University's objective of excellence in research, scholarship,
and education by publishing worldwide in

Oxford New York

Auckland Bangkok Buenos Aires Cape Town Chennai
Dar es Salaam Delhi Hong Kong Istanbul Karachi Kolkata
Kuala Lumpur Madrid Melbourne Mexico City Mumbai Nairobi
São Paulo Shanghai Taipei Tokyo Toronto

Oxford is a registered trade mark of Oxford University Press
in the UK and in certain other countries

British Library Cataloguing in Publication Data

Data available

ISBN 0 19 919645 1

1 3 5 7 9 10 8 6 4 2

Mixed Pack (1 of 6 different titles): ISBN 0 19 919647 8
Class Pack (6 copies of 6 titles): ISBN 0 19 919646 X

Illustrated by Derek Brazell c/o Artist Partners
Cover photo by Frank Camhi/Vision/Retna Pictures

Acknowledgements
p6 Spice Girls/Retna Pictures; p12 Retna Pictures; p13 Tim
Rooke (ROO)/Rex Features; p15 Eugene Adebari (EUG)/Rex
Features; p10 Rex Features; p11 Murray Andrew/Sygma/Corbis
UK Ltd.; p14 Nils Jorgensen (NJ)/Rex Features; p15 SIPA PRESS
(SIPA)/Rex Features; p40 Bouzad/Aitkins (ZZ)/Rex Features;
p43 S.I.N./Corbis UK Ltd.; p45 Richard Young (RY)/Rex Features;
p46 (top) Corbis UK Ltd.; p46 (bottom) Corbis UK Ltd.;
p47 (top) Brian Rasic (BRA)/Rex Features; p47 (centre)
Crollalanza (ADC)/Rex Features; p47 (bottom) Brian Rasic
(BRA)/Rex Features.

Printed in China

Contents

Introduction

Melanie Brown (Mel B) is one of five singer-dancers who became the world-famous *Spice Girls*. She had dreamed of fame since she was quite small and worked hard to achieve her goal all through primary school, secondary school, and college.

But it wasn't easy. Throughout, she had to battle against people who were jealous of her talent and rude about her skin colour.

It took a long time for her to get used to this and to be happy to stand up and be proud of what she was and strongly declare, "This is me. I'm **mixed race.**"

You can read lots about Mel B on the internet. These are some of the facts, woven into a story about Mel B. It tells of what it was like to grow up mixed-race, to be bullied, to be unhappy, and in spite of all of this, to grow up happy, successful, and to achieve the fame that she had always dreamed of.

Melanie Brown

A young Mel smiles for the camera

"Melanie Brown," announced the stage manager, who was standing by the stage curtain, motioning her towards the stage. Melanie Brown was so accustomed to being called just plain 'Mel' by everyone, that it took a little while for it to sink in that it was now *her* turn to perform her dance routine.

Mel had worked very hard for the show. She had practised in her breaks at school. She had practised in the front room when she got home, before and after her tea. She had even practised in her bedroom before going to sleep. It seemed that the only room she hadn't practised in, was the bathroom – because there just wasn't enough space! Mel had practised hard, not just because she wanted to be good in the show, but because she simply loved dancing.

From where she stood behind the curtains, the stage seemed a large and unfriendly place. She looked out into the audience but the lights had been dimmed and all she could see was a vague sea of unfamiliar, unsmiling faces. Desperately, she scanned the crowd for her mum and dad and Danielle, her little sister. They had brought her to the hall, so she knew they were there, but where?

"Melanie Brown," scolded the stage manager, "it's your turn. Get on stage!"

Mel took a deep breath and nervously stepped on to the stage. Immediately, there was wild enthusiastic applause from a small cluster of people at the front. It was her mum and dad, and Danielle and some of her neighbours and two of her mum's friends from work!

That started the rest of the audience clapping. Melanie relaxed; a broad smile creased her face. The pianist struck up the familiar tune she had practised to.

Mel launched into her tap routine. "I mustn't forget the steps," she said to herself. But the only thing she forgot was her nervousness. Soon she wasn't even thinking about the steps. All she could hear was the music and the sound of her shoes tapping in time to the rhythm and all she felt was a wonderful sensation of freedom and joy.

Little Mel feels the beat!

A grown up Mel B feels the same sensations of freedom and joy that she did as a child on stage

She got so caught up in the dance that she didn't even fully realise that she had stopped, that there was loud applause from the audience, and that her mum and dad and Danielle were clapping harder and longer than the rest.

"Melanie Brown!" a voice came from the side of the stage. It was the stage manager.

"Bow," she said, imitating the motion of someone bowing.

"Oh, dear, I almost forgot!" thought Mel. She took several deep bows, before leaving the stage, the applause still ringing in her ears.

Mel walked home happily between her parents, holding their hands. Some people stared, but Mel didn't notice. To her it was the most natural thing in the world to have a white mother and a black father.

A proud moment for Mel as she accepts an award in 1999 for her contribution to British Black music

"Melanie Brown, Brown Melanie"

The next morning in Assembly, the head teacher commended the children who had taken part in the show. She singled out Mel for special praise. Then at playtime, none of the friends that she usually hung out with wanted to play with her. Even her best friend, Samantha, pretended that she wasn't there.

"You're just a big show off," said one girl.

"People only clapped last night because they feel sorry for you."

"They feel sorry for you because you are a Paki. A frizzy-haired Paki!"

Mel had never been called a 'Paki' before and she had no idea what they meant. "What's a Paki? I'm not one, whatever it is," she protested.

"Yes, you are!" said a boy. "All Pakis are brown, and you are brown. That's why your name is Melanie Brown. So there!"

Mel was stunned into silence. What was wrong with being brown?

The children treated her silence as proof of victory. "Melanie Brown, Brown Melanie, Melanie Brown, Brown Melanie," they chanted, over and over again. They only stopped when the bell went for classes. Mel knew what it felt like to be saved by the bell.

When Mel went home she went straight to her room and locked the door. She threw herself on her bed and cried her eyes out. After much persuasion, she stomped stormily downstairs for dinner.

"What's wrong with my little princess?" asked her dad in his soft Caribbean accent.

She sat down glumly at the table, folded her arms and angrily asked, "Why do they call me a Paki?"

"So, they've been calling you names at school," her dad said in a matter of fact way. Mel was taken aback that her dad had figured out so quickly why she was upset. But she didn't understand why he wasn't angry. Didn't he know what she had been through?

"They've been calling me brown and a Paki and all sorts of names," she blurted out. "Why is it bad to be brown and what's a Paki?"

"Paki is just a short way of saying Pakistani, which means someone from Pakistan," her dad explained.

"So you see it's not as bad as you may think! They call Australians 'Aussies' and they don't seem to mind," her mum added.

"But Mum," Mel protested, "they make Paki sound like a really bad word. They make it sound like dirt. They even said all Pakis are brown, same as my name. So I must be a Paki."

"There's nothing wrong with being brown or being Pakistani," added her mum. "Some nasty people call anyone who isn't white a Paki – even when they are say, Indian or, like you, mixed race."

"They said my dad was *black*. They said that was even worse than being brown."

"I don't mind if people say I'm black, brown, yellow or even green," Dad said with a chuckle. "I just like my own colour however people want to describe it."

Mum chuckled too, as if suddenly the whole business of skin colour and skin tone seemed ridiculous. "When I met your dad, I fell in love with him straightaway. He was polite and treated me with kindness. And he made me laugh, which I really liked! But it split up our families because neither my parents or your dad's parents could accept it. They didn't think that people

from different races should mix. But nothing was going to tear us apart. So we decided to move away. We didn't have much money and we had to move into a little one bedroom flat."

The memory of it made Dad laugh. "It was the most damp, dingy place you could imagine, but we had each other

and that was all that counted. It was
Christmas time," he recalled, "and after
we had paid the deposit and the rent, all
we could afford for our Christmas
dinner was a tin of baked beans. But
your mum is right, we were as happy as
could be."

Mum then picked up the story, "Soon our families realised that nothing was going to tear us apart and by the time we got married at a register office, a lot of pride had been swallowed on both sides."

"And you are the result of that story," added Dad. "My little princess."

Mel felt suddenly better. "What's for dinner?" she asked.

"It's fish and chips – and baked beans!" said her mum, with a smile. "Your favourite."

Fact File

Full name :	Melanie Janine Brown
Date of Birth:	29th May 1975
Eye colour:	Brown
Height:	1m 66
Star sign:	Gemini
Home town:	Leeds, UK
Favourite colour:	Yellow
Favourite food:	Fish and Chips
Favourite music:	Rap, Hip-Hop, and Reggae
Hobbies:	Talking
School nickname:	Pineapple head
Dad's job:	Engineer
Mum's job:	Shop assistant

CHAPTER

3

A Prayer for Danielle

The name-calling continued. Mel was still made to feel different and she was often left out of games. But things were not bleak at school all the time, for there was always dancing and singing.

In the playground she would sometimes hold a pen or magic marker in her hand and pretend that it was a microphone and that she was a pop star singing into it. Sometimes other girls would join in the pretend game with her and because Mel was good at writing the words for songs and coming up with the tune, she would have moments of popularity and happiness. But something always happened to burst the bubble. Usually it was the school bell calling them back to classes, or some argument about who should sing what, or some silly remark that caused an argument. Then Mel was on her own again.

Mel was happy when Danielle was old enough to come to the school. Now at least she was not the only brown girl in school. But when they started to tease and bully Danielle too, it just broke her heart. How could anyone be mean to her

beautiful little sister? It really baffled Mel, who thought she would never learn to understand the strange ways of the world.

One day, when comforting Danielle again after the bullies' taunts, she cradled her little sister in her arms, looked at her colour and her hair and her eyes, and scowled. She then closed her eyes and prayed: "Please God, please make Danielle wake up tomorrow with white skin, blue eyes and blond hair, so that she won't have to suffer what I've been through."

When she opened her eyes she noticed
that Danielle was praying for the same
thing too. She could guess by the look
on her upturned face, the way she
clasped her hands together, and the
silent movement of her lips.

But the next morning, nothing had
changed. Danielle was still brown, with
brown eyes and with frizzy hair. Mel was
bitterly disappointed, but she didn't
really give much thought to how she
would have felt if Danielle had really

turned white overnight. What a shock it would have been. It wouldn't have been Danielle. It would have been like having a total stranger for a sister. How freaky would that be!

Mel and Danielle are as close today as when they were children

This is Me!

Mel B out and about

The years passed by and bit by bit, Mel and Danielle began to feel more comfortable with who they were. The warm applause when they performed in public helped. It was as if when they were on stage, nobody noticed their colour, or if they did, they certainly liked what they saw.

31

One day when she was just thirteen, something happened that made Mel really stop and think. It helped her to shape the way she viewed both herself and Danielle.

It was a sunny Saturday afternoon and she was in one of the shopping malls in Leeds town centre. Her long hair hung in loose curls over her shoulders and she was in a good mood. She was in a boutique trying on a pair of jeans when the shop assistant, a white girl, came up to her.

"How do you get your hair like that?" she asked.

"What do you mean?" asked Mel, who thought the girl was criticising her hair.

Then the girl added, "I have tried so many **perms** to get my hair like yours, but nothing I do really works."

Mel laughed. "I don't know. I don't use anything. That is just how it is."

The very same day, as she was on her way back home with her shopping bags, a black girl stopped her and asked, "How can I get my hair like yours?"

Mel laughed again. To be asked the same question twice on the same day, once by a white girl and once by a black girl was strange indeed. She gave the same answer, "I don't know, this is just how it is."

Walking home, she thought about it. "People do like the way I look," she thought. "And I look like I do because

The grown up Mel B is very comfortable with who and what she is. She loves to experiment with her look!

of who I am." The time had come to stand up for who and what she was. She had a loving family with a white mother and a black father, she had two rich cultures – one Caribbean and one British, and she was not going to let anyone force her to choose between them. They were both hers. "Say it out loud," she said. "I'm mixed race and I'm proud!"

Mel B and friends having a laugh

She had black friends and white friends, and she was not going to play up to any petty differences between them. She knew this was going to be the really difficult bit. For sometimes when she was with her black friends, they would put white people down and

expect her to join in. The reverse would happen when she was with those of her white friends who knew nothing about black history or the suffering black people had been through, and couldn't understand why black people were sometimes so angry.

CHAPTER

5

Mel B

Mel really wanted to succeed in the
world of show business and decided that
the best place to be for that was
London. So at the age of nineteen, she
got ready to leave home. It was difficult
to say goodbye to her mum and dad.

They were worried about Mel going off to live in a city so much bigger than Leeds, but they knew she had dreams of fame and fortune and that it would be foolish to stand in her way. But it was twice as difficult for Mel to say goodbye to Danielle.

Mel worried about Danielle; she thought of herself not only as her older sister but as her protector. Danielle read her thoughts. "Don't worry, Mel, I'll be all right. You take care of yourself."

Mel B and Mel C at a launch party in London, 2000

In London, Mel worked hard to get a break into show business. She appeared in the TV soap, *Coronation Street*, and also danced for a music group where she met a talented girl singer and dancer called Melanie Chisholm. They became great friends and ended up sharing a room together.

One day they saw an advert in a magazine, which read: *"R.U. 18-23 with the ability to sing/dance. R.U. streetwise, outgoing, ambitious and dedicated?"*

"That sounds just up our street!" Mel said to her room mate.

Four hundred girls applied and just five were chosen. Melanie Brown and Melanie Chisholm were amongst them. When they got the news they screamed and jumped for joy.

But then the hard work really started. They joined the other three girls in a house in Berkshire where they were taught lots of songs and special dance routines. The other three girls were called Geri Halliwell, Victoria Adams and Emma Bunton. Together, they called themselves the *Spice Girls*.

After months of hard practice, the girls released their first album called *Spice* which instantly became an international hit. Their first single, *Wannabe*, went to Number 1 in twenty-one countries!

Mel was over the moon. Neither she nor any of the other girls dared dream of such success. They were suddenly **celebrities** and their pictures were in almost all the newspapers everyday.

The Spice Girls in 1996

Phoenix from the Ashes

The life of a successful pop star was both thrilling and tiring. Sometimes Mel wished she could go back to being that simple girl in Leeds. But at other times she knew she would not have changed one thing in her life.

One of the most important things was the birth of her daughter, Phoenix Chi, shortly after her marriage to *Spice Girls* dancer, Jimmy Gulzar.

The world had changed so much since Mel was a small, scared girl in primary school. She couldn't imagine that when Phoenix was older, she could ever suffer the bullying that she and Danielle had.

Now that Danielle had gone on to feature in the popular TV soap, *Emmerdale*, Mel felt that life was good for her and her family, and she wanted to make sure that it stayed that way.

But just to make sure, one day as Phoenix was in her playpen, Mel took her in her arms. She swore silently to herself that she would never let any of the bad things that had happened to her and Danielle cause the same pain and uncertainty to Phoenix. She closed her eyes and prayed hard.

Mel B with her beloved daughter, Phoenix

The Spice Girls

The two Melanies were known as Mel B and Mel C to distinguish them, but it was a teen magazine which gave them their nicknames: Posh, Ginger, Sporty, Baby, and Scary Spice.

THE SPICE GIRLS

Mel C was "Sporty Spice" because of her athletic abilities.

SPORTY SPICE

Emma Bunton was "Baby Spice" because she was the youngest.

BABY SPICE

Mel B who was dubbed "Scary Spice". She didn't mind one bit if people thought she could be scary – they would probably think twice about trying to bully her!

SCARY SPICE

Victoria Adams was "Posh Spice" because it was thought she'd been well brought up.

POSH SPICE

Geri was "Ginger Spice" because of her vibrant red hair.

GINGER SPICE

Index

Glossary

celebrities famous people

mixed race having parents
of different races

perms permanent wave